THE LITTLE BOOK FOR WILD SWIMMERS

summersdale

LAURA SILVERMAN

THE LITTLE BOOK FOR WILD SWIMMERS

An Hachette UK Company
www.hachette.co.uk

Summersdale Publishers Ltd
Part of Octopus Publishing Group Limited
Carmelite House
50 Victoria Embankment
LONDON
EC4Y 0DZ
UK

www.summersdale.com

Printed and bound in Poland

ISBN: 978-1-83799-207-2

Substantial discounts on bulk quantities of Summersdale books are available to corporations, professional associations and other organizations. For details contact general enquiries: telephone: +44 (0) 1243 771107 or email: enquiries@summersdale.com.

Contents

Introduction 4

A note on safety 6

Mind 8

Body 32

Spirit 56

Lake 80

River 106

Sea 130

Conclusion 152

My dip list 154

Introduction

Nature is a balm for the mind, body and soul – and nothing comes close to the exhilaration of wild swimming. Whether you've already taken the plunge or simply want to dip a toe in, the great outdoors is waiting for you. Wild swimming in itself is not entirely new – lakes, rivers and seas have long lent themselves to a dip, a plunge, a bathe, a float, a splash, a splosh and a race. But it's only recently that we've begun to really appreciate just how much a swim in nature can help us take a vital pause from the fast pace of life and incessant demands of technology. Wild swimming encourages us to disconnect from daily stress and pay attention to the present moment. We can listen to the swish of the water and feel its resistance. We can watch birds absorbed in projects, building a nest or feeding their young. We can float to relax, gazing up at the clouds, or dart through the water as we channel our inner dolphin. Wild swimming connects us with our environment. It puts us at one with the world. It sets us free.

Best of all, if we swim in cold water – anything below 15°C (59°F) – experts believe we might reap extra rewards. Studies are starting to show that the cold could significantly boost our mental and physical health. To find out more about wild swimming and all its benefits, take a deep breath and dive in...

A note on safety

The idea that we could come across a lake, stroll along a river or skip along a coast and take a spontaneous swim sounds wonderfully carefree. This gentle warning is not meant to dampen that spirit. It's just a reminder of what to consider before, during and after a swim, so that we can fully, and safely, enjoy the experience.

- Ask locals about your proposed spot. Approach lifeguards, sailing clubs, surfers and swimmers. Do they know whether the river is prone to flash flooding or whether rip currents are common at the beach? Make sure you are aware of the state of the tides.

- Take a friend, even if they don't get in the water, as they can help you out of trouble or call for assistance, should you need it.

- Consider your swimming strength and know your limits. It's harder to swim in open water than at a pool, as you probably won't be able to touch the bottom or grab the side when you feel tired or get cramp.
- Avoid diving in, unless you are sure of the depth of water and confident that no hidden obstacles lie beneath the surface.
- Be prepared for cold-water shock. Don't stay in too long and get out of the water if your fingers stiffen – a sign you've become too cold.
- Warm up quickly afterward. You can start to shiver and feel light-headed after you get out, even if you initially felt fine.
- Seek medical advice before going wild swimming if you have heart disease, an irregular heartbeat, angina or untreated high blood pressure.

MIND

If you're lucky enough to stumble across a pod of bathers at the water's edge, they will flood you with reasons why they love wild swimming: it gives them energy. It clears their head. It connects them with nature. It makes them feel part of a community. For many, a plunge in cold water helps to manage stress. For those going through challenging times, it offers perspective. These claims might be enough to persuade you to immediately dive in, but don't just rely on these anecdotes; experts have been looking into wild swimming, too. Read on to discover how wild swimming really is good for you.

Feel alive

Plunge into water below 15°C (59°F) and feel ridiculously alive: lethargy disappears and sluggishness scurries away. This is because cold water activates our sympathetic nervous system, our fight-or-flight response, flooding us with the stress hormones adrenaline, noradrenaline and cortisol. Within the first minute of a dip, we feel a gush of energy. It might feel like a more intense version of splashing cold water on your face in the morning, but with longer-lasting effects. It might sound hard to believe, but a plunge into cold water will soon become addictive (in a good way), leaving you desperate to dive in again.

GET A
NATURAL HIGH

Cold water boosts our levels of dopamine –
the brain chemical behind our drive,
motivation and feelings of reward – by a
staggering 500 per cent. This natural high
lasts for up to four hours. The cold also
causes a release of beta-endorphins and
serotonin, our happy hormones, further
improving our mood. In one UK study, 61
people who learned to swim in cold water
over ten weeks reported a greater sense of
well-being than friends and relatives who
watched them from the shore.

Practise mindfulness

Experts might still be working out exactly why wild swimming makes so many people feel less anxious and depressed, but many swimmers have discovered that a dip is the perfect opportunity to practise mindfulness, which helps to ease anxiety and depression. The bracing cold makes us pay attention to the moment, and we become hyperaware of our tingling limbs and frozen noses. We can't think about anything else. The cold is a possessive beast, and it will not share its space with anything else. If everyday concerns intrude, the cold is ready to push them away, bringing us back to the here and now, and helping us to emerge from the water with a new perspective. When we're more used to the cold, or on a warmer day, wild swimming gives us the chance to practise mindfulness in other ways. We might like to concentrate on our breath, counting down from 20. Or lie on our backs and do a body scan, gradually bringing our attention to each part, from our toes to our head. Alternatively, we could focus on an element of our surroundings: the light dancing on the water or the breeze swishing through the grass.

RELAX

It might seem strange that cold water can relax us, but it does so by helping our body deal with stress. The shock of the cold makes us take short, sharp breaths and our sympathetic nervous system kicks in, triggering our flight-or-fight response. We can overcome these short, sharp breaths by taking deep, deliberate ones from our diaphragm. Deep breathing, also known as belly breathing, is soothing: it slows down our heart rate and lowers or stabilizes our blood pressure. This breathing activates the parasympathetic nervous system, the network of nerves that relaxes us. By focusing on breathing deeply and rhythmically, wild swimming becomes much like meditation on the move.

Once we've adjusted to the cold and feel ready, we can stimulate the parasympathetic nervous system even more by putting our face underwater. This activates the diving reflex, waking up the vagus nerve, one of its key components. Triggering our parasympathetic nervous system, as well as our sympathetic one, creates conflict in our body. This controlled form of stress gives our nervous system a workout. We are training ourselves to become more comfortable in stressful situations, including our next dip in cold water.

Swimming is a rite
of passage, a crossing
of boundaries.

ROGER DEAKIN

Set your mind free

There's a freedom that comes with wild swimming. We don't have to contend with answering emails, tidying away dishes or picking up dirty washing off the floor. Once we have adjusted to our watery conditions, we might slip into a state of "flow". The term was coined in the early 1970s by Mihaly Csikszentmihalyi, a Hungarian-American psychologist. When you're in flow, he said "the self seems to fall away". We become wholly engaged in what we're doing. Flow gives us a break from our daily stress, fears and anxieties.

Spark your creativity

The late neurologist and writer Oliver Sacks swam nearly every day, attributing his creativity to his daily dip. After each swim, he would record the ideas that had come to him in the water. Sometimes, he said, they even arrived in full paragraphs, and there's good reason for this – wild swimming encourages creativity in many forms. Being in the water forces us to disconnect from technology and, as we ease into our strokes or float, we daydream. The brain areas associated with a resting state are activated, which helps us to make different connections and come up with fresh ideas.

Embrace the awe

Wild swimming can be intense. The
watery environment is very different
from our routine lives. How often do
we subject ourselves to temperatures
that are bone-chillingly cold or
immerse ourselves in a body of water
so mysteriously deep we can't see
the bottom? Or glide harmoniously
alongside marine creatures as if we
were guests in their home? Like the
Romantics of the eighteenth century,
we might experience the "sublime",
a feeling of transcendence and awe.
This encounter with the natural
world can give us a real thrill.

GROW YOUR CONFIDENCE

If you've ever slipped into a lake, unsure of the temperature or what's lurking below, or you've swum out halfway and doubted you have the energy to make it back, you'll know the sense of self-satisfaction and achievement that comes afterwards. Wild swimming boosts our self-esteem and we feel more confident when we emerge.

We might be mentally stronger in another way, too. Experts think that swimming in cold water can make us more emotionally resilient because of "cross-stress adaptation". This is because our body experiences the cold as a form of stress. While long-term stress can be damaging, an acute bout of stress (such as that caused by cold water) might be useful. By subjecting ourselves to a little stress in the water, we are training ourselves to deal with stress in other forms in our lives. We will be better able to face work deadlines or cope with family arguments, as well as approaching challenges more calmly and recovering more quickly.

Embrace eco-therapy

Wild swimming is the ultimate eco-therapy, as many believe that being in nature improves our mental health. We might even think of it as "eco-therapy plus" because submerging ourselves in the water enables us to experience the natural world on its own terms. We engage with it completely as we surrender to the elements. When we're in the sea or in the middle of a lake, we might feel especially at one with the environment, surrounded by water as far as the eye can see. Opening our minds, we may experience the "oceanic feeling" described by the French writer Romain Rolland in a letter to Sigmund

Freud, the founder of psychoanalysis, in the nineteenth century. Rolland used the phrase to describe "a sensation of eternity" or "being one with the external world". He had been inspired by the teachings of Ramakrishna, an Indian Hindu mystic. Rolland and Freud explored "the oceanic feeling" as the source of religious energy. But swimmers today understand that you don't have to be religious to experience it. We can get that relaxed, expansive feeling whenever we're in touch with our surroundings. In the water, we realize that we're part of something bigger than ourselves.

Explore
blue spaces

Spending 20 minutes regularly in or near blue spaces – large bodies of water – boosts our long-term well-being. "Blue mind theory", developed by marine biologist Wallace J. Nichols, suggests that being around water encourages a gentle meditative state. Its blue hue may well be important: according to colour psychology, we associate it with feelings of peace and tranquillity. Watching the ocean has also been shown to increase alpha waves in our brain, which are those produced when we're calm. Moreover, listening to the crash of waves or lapping water switches on our parasympathetic nervous system, the network of nerves that relaxes us.

THE BEST TIME FOR NEW BEGINNINGS IS NOW

By the light
of the moon

Taking a moonlight dip has a special thrill: the reduced visibility pushes us out of our comfort zone and heightens our other senses. As we bathe under the stars, we might even channel some ancient wisdom, reflecting on our human achievements and feeling restored by the light of the silvery moon.

Enjoy a safer midnight swim

- Do the swim in daylight first, so you know the potential hazards.
- Make yourself visible. Place a torch inside a tow float or clip a waterproof safety light to the back of your goggles.
- Bring extra layers for afterward. Air cools faster than water at night.
- Plan how to dress in the dark. Arrange your clothes so you can put them on quickly.

BE A SUSTAINABLE SWIMMER

When we go wild swimming, we're at one with nature, so it makes sense to look after it. Follow these tips to respect our much-loved watery environment:

- Choose long-lasting swimwear that will have a lower impact on the environment, as you'll help to minimize textile waste.
- Use a marine-safe sunscreen brand.
- Invest in reusable glow sticks, which you can attach to your wrist or the back of your head to help you be more visible, rather than standard disposable ones.
- Car-share to and from swimming locations.
- Tread carefully around plants, especially

when getting in and out of the water.

- Give nesting birds space, and keep clear of areas populated by breeding and spawning fish.
- Leave waterweed and gravel beds undisturbed.
- Clean up litter – your own and others'. Even better, organize a beach or riverbank clean.
- Take pictures of shells and pebbles rather than taking off with them.
- Remember to wash your wetsuit between different swimming locations to stop the spread of invasive species.

Find your pod

In the dolphin world, being part of a group is everything. A group or pod of dolphins travel together, playing, hunting, looking out for predators and caring for each other's young. Take up wild swimming and you'll instantly become part of your own pod: a community of like-minded people of all ages and from all backgrounds bonded by their shared love of wild swimming. Groups swim together regularly and may well share tips online. Search for your local one on Facebook or Meetup.

Swimming with others is usually safer, as you'll be able to keep an eye on each other, and long-timers can share their experiences and the best spots. Aside from the support offered by a group and the pleasure of company, studies show that people with close social ties tend to have lower blood pressure, fewer heart problems and better mental health. They even live longer, which means more years of wild swimming and bonding afterward over flasks of hot tea.

BODY

Cold-water bathing has been in vogue for centuries. In the fifth century BCE, Hippocrates recommended it to ease fatigue. In the eighteenth century, Dr Richard Russell, a British physician, championed seawater bathing for ailments ranging from scurvy to gland conditions. Experts today think they may have been onto something. Cold water, below 15°C (59°F), may boost immunity, reduce chronic pain and improve circulation. Small doses are best. We need to allow our bodies to adjust to the cold and recognize signs that we should return to the warmth, as staying in too long can lead to hypothermia.

ALL THE GEAR

Roman soldiers swam in full armour, but you don't need to go that far. However, depending on where you swim, you might like to supplement your bikini or trunks with some cold-water kit. Check out this shopping list for items that might make your cold-water swim a little more comfortable and safer:

- Wetsuit for added buoyancy and warmth.
- Brightly coloured swim cap and tow float for visibility.
- Swim gloves and boots for warmth.
- Goggles with UV lenses to protect your eyes from harmful ultraviolet radiation from the sun, especially as its rays reflect off the water.
- Whistle to attract attention if you, or a swim buddy, get into trouble.
- Compass – especially at night or in fog.

Health boost

The actress Katharine Hepburn swam daily in the Pacific Ocean to fend off colds – and research supports her thinking. In one study in Germany, regular swimmers in ice-cold water had 40 per cent fewer upper respiratory infections, such as colds and bronchitis, than non-swimmers. Cold-water immersion boosts the immune system by encouraging it to produce white blood cells, which fight bacteria and viruses, as well as antioxidants, which protect cells from free radicals (molecules linked to conditions from heart disease to cancer). Similar research has found that people who ended their shower with a 30-second blast of cold water took fewer sick days.

NOT ALL FAT
IS EQUAL

Brown fat is a type of healthy fat stored around the spine. Unlike white fat, it gets its colour from mitochondria, small structures in the cells that produce energy and heat. This type of fat regulates our temperature, revs up our metabolism and can help our blood sugar response or insulin sensitivity. But although we're born with a lot of it (babies need it to keep warm because they can't shiver), we lose it with age unless we use it. When we go for a dip in cold water, we activate our sympathetic nervous system, which increases noradrenaline, a hormone that turns white fat into brown. This warms us up and gives us energy. Danish metabolic scientist Dr Susanna Søberg has spent years looking at brown fat and found some incredible benefits, all activated just by going into water a little colder than our skin (no ice baths required). In the short term, our brown fat acts as an inner heater, keeping us warm. In the long term, having more brown fat could lower our risk of type 2 diabetes, obesity, high cholesterol and high blood pressure.

Inflammation

British anaesthetist Dr Mark Harper believes cold-water swimming could help reduce inflammation, which could underpin a range of conditions from arthritis and type 2 diabetes to depression and dementia. The immediate anti-inflammatory benefit comes from the diving reflex. Dipping our face underwater stimulates our vagus nerve, the main component of our parasympathetic nervous system, which helps to control inflammation. The long-term benefit comes from swimming more often. Going into cold water puts stress on our bodies, but after six immersions, we start to adapt. This helps us to respond to a range of stress, from physical stress like inflammation to psychological stress in our daily lives.

Pain management

For many with physical pain, cold-water swimming can offer a welcome respite. It can ease arthritic aches by stimulating blood circulation, lowering pressure on sore joints and reducing inflammation. It might ease other forms of pain – from migraines to fibromyalgia (a little understood condition characterized by chronic pain and muscle stiffness all over the body) – in a more radical way. Dr Mark Harper has suggested that the shock of cold water could reset our brain's electronic circuits by overwhelming them. Even if a swim doesn't create physical change, it will at least distract us from our pain for a few minutes.

Get a glow-up

Any sort of exercise will boost
our circulation and leave us with
a healthy glow. But wild swimming
has added perks. We may well look
especially refreshed, as cold water
tightens pores and reduces puffiness.
Warmer water has advantages, too. Warm
seawater can ease psoriasis, loosening
flaky skin cells, while the salt can
lower inflammation and irritation.
The sea, whatever the temperature,
can also soothe eczema. This is because
the magnesium in the water can help
the skin to retain moisture.

The anti-ageing effect

Wild swimming might give us a boost of youthful energy, but can it really turn back the clock? Not exactly, but experts believe it might help to stave off age-related diseases. One British study looking at regular cold-water swimmers found they had a protein called RBM3 that slows the onset of dementia and repairs some of the damage – albeit in mice. More research still needs to be done and older people should check with a doctor before embarking on a cold plunge.

Renew thyself
completely each day;
do it again, and again,
and forever again.

HENRY DAVID THOREAU

Thrill of the chill

Almost everyone experiences cold-water shock in temperatures below 15°C (59°F). The water cools our skin, stimulating the cold receptors under its surface. Our heart rate and blood pressure shoot up. We gasp. We might want to hyperventilate. It can feel like a panic attack, but it doesn't have to become one. Cold-water shock lasts a couple of minutes, decreasing with regular swims. Make sure you enter the water slowly, and try splashing your face and neck to lower the impact of the cold. Take deep breaths into your belly and keep your head above water until your breathing is under control. Try to do this at a depth where you can easily stand to avoid inhaling any water or panicking.

Cold-water taster

Cold water can come as a shock on your first few wild swims, but with preparation and determination, you will soon get used to it. As a "cold-water taster", try having cold showers. Then make the initial few dips short. Notice how your body reacts to the water in different weather. Wearing a wetsuit, and neoprene socks, gloves and cap will help you to retain body heat, allowing you to swim for longer, although those items won't offer total cold protection. Look out for "swim failure", when our nerves and muscles cool, slowing our nerve impulses and making muscles stiff. We become less coordinated and might find our legs dip in the water when we're horizontal, making it nearly impossible to swim. Our arms are especially vulnerable to the cold because they have a high surface-to-mass ratio. Our fingers might spread out and we might develop "claw hand", meaning that our fingers start to curl up and we can't straighten them. This is an important sign that it's time to get out of the water and warm up. Exit slowly to avoid feeling faint or dizzy. The risk of swim failure lowers as we become used to the cold, making it possible to swim for longer.

HYPOTHERMIA

Hypothermia sets in when our deep tissues cool to 35°C (95°F), compared to our normal core temperature of 36.5–37°C (97.7–98.6°F). It's rare for swimmers to develop full-blown hypothermia, where you fall unconscious, in under 30 minutes, but symptoms can creep up. Look out for "the umbles": the grumbles (a dismal outlook), stumbles (stiff joints), fumbles (poor coordination) and mumbles (you can't speak clearly). You could also start feeling confused. In cold temperatures, swim for no longer than the number of degrees Celsius of the water. For example, if the water is 3°C, make sure you enjoy a swim for no longer than three minutes.

Hypothermia action plan

- Get out of the water.
- Remove wet swimwear.
- Pat skin and hair dry (rubbing can damage skin).
- Dress in dry clothes, with a hat and gloves.
- Go indoors or find somewhere sheltered from the wind.
- Sip a warm, sweet drink.
- Walk around or do some gentle movements, such as circling your arms or lifting up your knees.
- Wait until you have completely warmed up before driving home.
- For severe symptoms, call the emergency services.

BEWARE "AFTERDROP"

You're out of the water and you feel great. So why, five, 15, 30 minutes later, do you now feel cold? The fall in our core temperature at this stage is called "afterdrop" and it's all to do with circulation. When we emerge, the warmer blood in our core hurries to the muscles and tissues in our body that are especially cold, on a vital mission to heat them up. The cooler blood then moves to our core, and our brain thinks our bodies are getting colder.

Your "afterdrop" action plan

- Dress quickly. Start by putting on your top first, as this will warm up your core and vital organs around the heart.

- Heat yourself up from the inside out by doing star-jumps, dancing or power-walking.
- Have a warm drink – although this is more for comfort, as the actual effect on body temperature is minimal.
- Take a lukewarm (not hot) shower. Keep the temperature dial on your shower in the middle. Hot water will open up your blood vessels, encouraging cooled blood to return faster to your core, making "afterdrop" worse.
- Hit the sauna. If you're lucky enough to have access to one, follow Nordic tradition and go to a sauna, as hot air is a safe way to warm up after a cool dip.

COLD ACCLIMATIZATION

After as few as six plunges in relatively quick succession, our bodies adjust to the cold. Professor Mike Tipton, who studies the effects of extreme environments on the body in the UK, has found we can halve cold-water shock with five three-minute head-out immersions over three days. Once we've acclimatized (experts suggest going at least once a week at first), the water won't necessarily feel warm, but we should be able to breathe more easily after just a couple of gasps. Don't worry if you've taken a break from wild swimming: cold habituation lasts more than a year.

Saving a struggling swimmer

Sometimes our brains overcommit and we push ourselves too far. If you spot a struggling swimmer, act quickly but calmly. First, reassure them and encourage them to move towards the shore. To help, hold out a branch, pole or piece of clothing to "reel" them in – ideally, from a secure spot on land. Alternatively, throw the swimmer a life ring or ball to make it easier for them to stay buoyant. A lifeguard might tow an exhausted swimmer to safety by putting one arm under their chin. Only hold a struggling swimmer as the last resort, as you could put your own life in danger.

The Wim Hof Method

Every morning, Dutch extreme athlete Wim Hof plunges into icy water for at least two or three minutes – and sometimes up to half an hour. Cold exposure, combined with deep breathing and willpower, Hof says, can improve your mood and energy, reduce stress and lower inflammation.

The same benefits can be reaped through cold-water swimming. The Wim Hof Method, which Hof formulated in 1995 as a radical way to cope with the death of his wife, is just a little more intense. It involves a regimented, daily practice of cold showers, breathing exercises and meditation. Some followers also repeat Hof's catchy mottos, such as "Breathe, motherf***er!" Hof's idea of a wild swim is wilder than most, with many of his 26 Guinness World Records involving the cold, including the longest swim under ice. But the popularity of his method is striking. Hof has an A-list fan base and millions of social media followers. He has also attracted serious interest from scientists. Hof's method is less about machismo and more about a new approach to well-being.

BREATHE IN COURAGE, BREATHE OUT FEAR

The no-exercise workout

Ordinarily, we might think going to the gym or heading out for a run is the only way to get a workout, but actually the initial shock of plunging into chilly water increases our blood pressure and heart rate. The cold causes our blood vessels to narrow, making the heart work harder to pump blood and oxygen around our bodies. If you already experience high blood pressure or heart problems, speak to your doctor before going for a dip. For others, the rise in blood pressure and heart rate could be a real benefit. The cold gives our cardiovascular system a workout. Over time, the heart should become more efficient, thus lowering our blood pressure and improving circulation.

SPIRIT

Water captivates us. Ancient cultures and world religions have revered it for thousands of years, believing it can cleanse our souls and restore us. Writers, artists and composers through the ages have been moved by the force, beauty and majesty of particular rivers, oceans and lakes. Swimming in these waters can stir something deep within us. It can help us to tap into a shared humanity, moving us in ways we hadn't expected. We don't need to follow a specific faith to experience its spiritual benefits; swimming can give us faith in ourselves – we just have to open ourselves up to its power.

Hidden depths

How vital water is to life: we drink it, we bathe in it, it grows our food. Yet it can also snatch life away. Floods can engulf our homes, storms can sink ships, accidents can result in drowning. Water is life-giving, while every so often reminding us of our mortality. We become acutely aware of this when we're swimming. Immersed, we can feel a womb-like security, while realizing that, physically at least, we are land animals – even if something always draws us back to the water.

Spiritual cleansing

Water is purifying and many of the world's main religions teach that it can wash away sins. Christians are baptized, often as babies. Hindus hold a huge festival – the Kumbh Mela, every 12 years – where millions bathe in the Ganges, the personification of the goddess Ganga. Muslims wash before prayer. In many cases, the meaning may be largely symbolic – a way to show we want to be forgiven and get closer to God, but the feeling goes much deeper. Bathing in water, whatever our faith or absence of one, makes us feel renewed. Seeping into our skin, it feels as though it cleanses us from the outside in.

The swim of your dreams

Has swimming snuck into your dreams? If so, you might want to consider what these images may mean. If you're drowning in a dream, you may be feeling overwhelmed by a work project or life admin. If you're floating, you might feel content in a relationship. If there's a flood, perhaps you're going through a time of renewal. To interpret your swimming dreams, try to adopt the Sigmund Freud method of "free association" and say what comes to mind when you replay what happened. Freud believed dreams were the disguised fulfilment of a wish. Your dreams of water could help you make sense of your life on land.

PORTALS TO ANOTHER WORLD

Can worshipping water connect us to a higher power? The Romans thought so. They would throw coins and jewellery into rivers as offerings to the gods for safe passage. The ancient Mayans, the Indigenous people of Mexico and Central America, took things further. They believed cenotes – sinkholes full of freshwater, mainly in the Yucatán peninsula – were gateways to the underworld. Their rain god, Chaak, lived below and, to please him, they threw gold, pottery and even people into the pools as sacrifices. You can still swim in many of these cenotes today.

The wonder of water

Like many religious and spiritual experiences, wild swimming can lead us to moments of wonder, meaning and even personal transcendence. We meld into our surroundings, feeling part of something bigger than ourselves. Rather than making us feel insignificant, this can be a comfort and a solace, as our responsibilities feel lighter and we realize we are not alone. Swimmers facing grief or going through a difficult time often say that being in the water helps to clear their head and put life into perspective. Sadness no longer overwhelms them. It might not lessen the pain, but it can offer the headspace to manage it.

Skinny-dipping

Skinny-dipping is about experiencing the sensuality of the water in the simplest, purest way, feeling the cold on parts of your body that are usually covered up and more sensitive to touch. It can be exhilarating to swim naked, making us feel carefree – and a little brave. Too shy to scamper bare-bottomed into the water? Why not take the plunge in your swimwear, before taking it off and tying it to your wrist? A quiet area, or nudist beach, is ideal to avoid shocking people on the shore.

GO WILD
FOR A
WHILE

Be inspired

Rebirth. Danger. Change. Water represents strong themes for many writers. Charles Kingsley grew up near the Dart, in Devon, a river that may well have inspired *The Water-Babies*. Alice Oswald used the same river for the bedrock of her poem, *Dart*, based on conversations with people nearby. The Mississippi runs through much American literature. It was a symbol of freedom for Huckleberry Finn, created by Mark Twain, who once drove a steamboat on the river; just as it was for Langston Hughes, who wrote one of his most popular poems, "The Negro Speaks of Rivers", when he was crossing it.

Water painters

Artists have long been fascinated by the elusive nature of water. Art critic John Ruskin, a fan of J. M. W. Turner's seafaring paintings, wrote of the near-impossibility of "giving surface to smooth water". David Hockney talked of the difficulty of painting something that is "movable", but many have risen to the challenge. In his famous work, *The Swimming Pool*, Henri Matisse depicted water's fluidity by cutting swimmers out of blue paper. Other artists have focused on the bathers themselves, including Thomas Eakins, whose male nudes have been seen as homoerotic, tapping into the sensuality we often feel when the watery waves wrap around us.

The Cave of Swimmers

In 1933, László Almásy, a Hungarian explorer, discovered what many think is the earliest record of wild swimming. The Cave of Swimmers, in Egypt, is about 9,000 years old. The walls inside are covered with drawings of Neolithic figures, some horizontal with their limbs bent as if mid-stroke. This suggests that swimming may well be part of our common humanity – part of what makes us us, regardless of background or culture. Going for a dip, we recognize what we share with others and connect to people in a deeper way, both around us and across space and time.

Keep a journal

Chart your swims in a beautiful notebook, capturing the sights, sounds, smells and sensations around you. Concentrating on each sense in turn will encourage you to focus on your experience of the here and now. Look for the unexpected and jot down how you feel before and after being in the water. Don't worry about crafting the perfect line of poetry, just let your ideas flow. Use the following page to start writing down your feelings and thoughts around water.

SWIM LIKE...
LORD BYRON

According to his mistress Lady Caroline Lamb, Lord Byron was "mad, bad and dangerous to know". To others, he was simply mad about swimming. Byron had a leg deformity and felt liberated in the water. He breast-stroked his way down the Thames and the Grand Canal in Venice, and in 1810, he swam the Hellespont: the 4.8 km (3 mi) stretch of water between Europe and Asia, known today as the Dardanelles in Turkey. Channel Byron's spirit wherever you swim: in the water, you can overcome anything – physical or psychological – that might be holding you back on land.

Swim like...
Jane Austen

Going for a dip was all the rage in Georgian England. Jane Austen's final, unfinished novel *Sanditon* is set in "a young and rising bathing-place", where one character praises the sea air and sea bathing as being "a match for every disorder". Writing to her sister in 1804, Jane raves about the "delightful" bathing that morning in Dorset, fearing she "staid in rather too long". Like others of the day, she would have put on her bathing gown in a "bathing machine" or wagon. A woman or "dipper" would then have wheeled the contraption – Jane included – towards the water, where she could submerge herself.

Swim like...
Iris Murdoch

Anglo-Irish novelist Iris Murdoch loved taking a dip in the Thames, near Oxford, where she lived. "The art is to draw no attention to oneself but to cruise quietly by the reeds like a water rat," she wrote. She saw swimming as spiritual, connecting her to nature. Swimming appears in many of her novels, from *Under the Net* to *The Sea, the Sea*. Swim like Murdoch by immersing yourself in the environment. Imagine how the grass on the banks might appear to an aquatic creature, towering above them, and tune into sounds they might hear – a stone skimming the water or the rustle of a leaf.

Books and
bathing have
a close affinity,
for the imagination
transforms both.

IRIS MURDOCH

Great composers

From watery myths to the majesty of the ocean, composers have long been swept up by the life aquatic. Some have turned to myths and legends, like Tchaikovsky in *Swan Lake*, while others have been inspired directly by trips to the water's edge. Mendelssohn wrote *The Hebrides* on a visit to Scotland, evoking the crashing waves by a cave. Debussy, who once said he longed to have been a sailor, wrote much of *La Mer* in Eastbourne, beside the English Channel. Water can affect all the senses – and the sound of it, from rolling waves to a gently trickling stream, can help with mindfulness and staying in the moment.

Snap away

Sketching a swim scene from the shore might sound romantic, but it's not always practical. What if it's very cold? What if you're not a fan of drawing? You could take pictures on your phone or a disposable underwater camera instead. Try not to think about taking a picture for social media or to show friends: make sure you take it for yourself. What is unique about this moment for you? Days, weeks or months later, you can look back at these images to tap into the specialness of that swim. Recall the serenity of the surroundings and remember the sheer joy of splashing about.

CRYSTAL MEDITATION

On days when you can't get to the water, channel the watery energy of the aquamarine crystal to get some of the same meditative benefits. This stone gets its name from the Latin *aqua marinus* for "seawater", due to its blue-green colour, and has been used for emotional healing and to promote inner calm for centuries. Try this simple meditation exercise:

- Find a quiet, comfortable spot.
- Close your eyes and take slow, deep breaths. Loosen your shoulders, relax tense muscles and feel stillness in the moment.
- Open your eyes and bring your awareness to the crystal.
- Note the shape, colour and texture. How does the light reflect off it?
- Tap into the peace you feel when you're in the water.
- Now resume your day with the benefit of watery calmness.

Dip list

You might aim to go wild swimming to escape your to-do list. But a dip list — a bucket list of places where you'd like to go — is different in that you'll want to tick off entries and yet won't want to reach the end. Making a dip list can keep you motivated and inspired, especially if you research the history and folklore of some of the spots. Do the Fairy Pools on the Isle of Skye provide a home to selkies, a human on land and seal in the water? Does the Ogopogo, a multi-humped beast, really lurk in Okanagan Lake in British Columbia?

RECORD A BEDTIME SOUNDTRACK

Listening to nature can reduce our levels of cortisol, the stress hormone, and relax us. Researchers have found that naturalistic sounds also quieten the sympathetic nervous system, which controls our fight-or-flight response, and increase the activity of the parasympathetic nervous system, the network of nerves that calms the body down after stress. Our breathing and heart rate slow down, too. Capture pink noise – the lapping waves, the flow of a stream or a waterfall – on your phone to replay back home or search on Spotify, creating your own soundscape for a bedtime meditation.

LAKE

Depending on where we live, we might call them lakes, lochs, loughs, lagoons, meres, ponds, tarns or reservoirs. Lochs, loughs and lagoons are inlets of the sea, but are often enclosed by land. Lakes are generally bigger than ponds, but not always. In Wisconsin, most ponds are called lakes. In Newfoundland, most lakes are called ponds. Whatever name you give them, all have clear appeal: they're usually relatively still, relatively safe bodies of water that seem less formidable than the high and mighty sea or a fast-flowing river, making them ideal destinations for a wild swim, regardless of whether you're a total newbie or cold-water connoisseur.

Choose your route

Unlike public pools, which have lanes, lakes can offer a bemusing array of routes. Should you swim the circumference or head for the middle? Get a sense of the lake's shape before you go in, identifying landmarks that will help you to get your bearings. Unless you're heading for the opposite shore or are avoiding hazards like rocks, swim parallel to the shore. It makes navigation easier and means you'll know how far it is back to land. In windy conditions, try to swim into waves at the start, when you have more energy. The waves will then be behind you on your return, making it easier to swim back.

How to see...

In a pool, you can swim in a straight line by following tiles or lane ropes. In a lake, you'll need to "sight", looking up to check your direction, as well as avoid boats, branches and birds. Pinpoint local landmarks, perhaps a distinctive building or cluster of trees on the shore. Then, pick one to aim for. Sight by lifting your head – or just your eyes – out of the water as you swim, taking quick mental snapshots of where you are. With a little practice, you'll sight automatically as you take your strokes.

THE GREATEST
REWARDS LIE
OUTSIDE OUR
COMFORT ZONE

Supervised swims

If you're not used to swimming in open water or long to go for a dip when your swim buddies aren't free, a supervised swimming spot might be the answer. These wild bodies of water, which can be in public parks or on country estates, farms or school grounds, have the benefit of being looked after. Many will have lifeguards, some will have a changing area and hot showers, and a few even have a cafe. They can be great places to meet like-minded people, too. If you can't find a local venue, you could go on a wild swim with a coach to help you build confidence in the water.

SAFE SWIMS

There really is nothing like swimming wild and free in a lake, discovering its unique features and drinking in the awesome views of mountains, fields or rolling hills. But however breathtaking your backdrop, you need to stay safe. Here are a few points to consider:

- Caught in weeds? Don't panic – just slide your limbs out the same way as they went in.

- Be prepared for the cold. Freshwater lakes tend to be cooler than the sea in winter. (The good news is they're usually warmer than the sea in the summer.)

- Expect changing temperatures at different depths in the same spot. In hotter months, water is warmer on the surface. In colder ones, when water is below 4°C (39°F), it will be chillier towards the top.

- Not yet acclimatized to the cold? Swim parallel to the shore for an easy exit.
- Avoid blue-green algae. These blooms, which look like paint on the water, can cause rashes and, if swallowed, can make you sick.
- Reduce your risk of swimmer's itch – a rash caused by a parasite – by rinsing exposed skin with clean water after a dip and drying it well.
- Soothe any rashes with a high-quality moisturizer or anti-itch cream, or have an Epsom salt bath.

Waves and currents

Lakes are not always as calm as they appear. Some – such as Lake Garda in Italy – experience standing waves or seiches, where factors like a strong wind sweep the water between shores, so that it swishes back and forth. Many have currents and if there's a sandbar, often underwater, linking the shore with rocks or an island, look out for a channel current moving parallel to the land. Caught up in it? Don't fight the flow by trying to grasp the sandbar; instead, swim towards the shore. If you can't, float and wave for help. If you're near a pier, watch out for structural currents. Here, water flows away from the shore alongside it. Swim wide of piers and don't leap off them.

Reservoirs

Reservoirs can make alluring swimming spots. Many are carefully managed, making the water relatively clean. Make sure you can get in and out easily – banks are often steep. And be prepared for sudden changes in depth, especially as it is hard to tell where these are from the shore. Don't enter by or swim near reservoir structures, including the dam wall, tower or spillway (where the water flows away from the reservoir). The undertow from sluices and pipes beneath the surface can pull you under. Avoid aerators too, as these inject bubbles into the water, making it hard to stay afloat.

A lake carries you into recesses of feeling otherwise impenetrable.

WILLIAM WORDSWORTH

SOME LIKE IT HOTTER

Hot or thermal springs come about when water seeps deep underground and circulates back up. In volcanic areas, like the Blue Lagoon in Iceland, water gets its heat from magma. The water, which is above 37°C (98.6°F), is rich in minerals such as calcium and sulphate. These can seep into the skin, so even if you're sold on the cold, a soak in hot water might have benefits. It could relax tense muscles, ease joint pain, boost circulation and help skin conditions. Drink plenty of water to avoid dehydration and seek medical advice if you're pregnant or have heart disease.

Deep-water fear

Even experienced swimmers can be struck by panic: what – or who – lurks in the water? Lakes are often filled with weeds, wildlife and, sadly, even litter that lurks unseen below the surface. When we experience fear, adrenaline and cortisol – the stress hormones – rush around our bodies, our hearts race and we gasp for air. All this means our fight-or-flight instinct, triggered by our sympathetic nervous system, has kicked in and our brain is telling us that we're in danger. Experiencing deep-water fear is a good sign: it means we're expanding our horizons, but we will want to overcome any anxiety and tell our brain we're safe.

Follow these tips to calm your fears:

- Take slow, deep breaths. Try ratio breathing – inhaling for four counts, holding for two and exhaling for six.
- Focus on your stroke. This distraction technique puts you back in control. Find a slower rhythm and engage your core strength.
- Repeat a mantra. Telling yourself you are calm over and over again is surprisingly effective.
- Star float. Lying back with your arms and legs spread slightly apart allows you to recover your breathing.

Be seen

Your tow float is your best friend in the water – especially in lakes, where other users can range from rowboats and motorboats to paddleboarders and canoeists, all with a varying range of experience captaining their vessels. A tow float is a brightly coloured inflatable buoy that you tie to your waist, so that it drags along lightly behind you. You might like the feeling of swimming untethered, but many find a float essential.

Visibility

Your tow float should help boats and other water users to spot you more easily, thus reducing the likelihood of accidents. Always swim with one in busier spots, in choppier water and on mistier days. If you're swimming at night, attach an adventure light to it or place one inside for your own water lantern.

Support
While it's not a life ring, a tow float will help you to stay afloat if you grow tired, get cramp, or want to pause for a chat or to take in your surroundings.

Storage
You can also tow clothes and valuables in your float if you're on a one-way trip or want to wander around on a different part of the shore. Don't forget to put your mobile phone inside for emergencies.

Improve your stroke

You don't have to be competing in a triathlon to want to improve your technique, as a more efficient stroke can help boost your stamina for longer adventures or make it easier to tackle swims in wind and rain. Front crawl (or freestyle) is popular for speed, but many wild swimmers prefer breaststroke, which conserves energy, or a mix of the two, depending on the conditions. (Avoid backstroke because it will be hard to see where you're going.) Focus on each movement in turn in the water. Back on land, a simple Pilates workout can help to strengthen your core and increase flexibility.

WASTWATER, ENGLAND

Overcome any fear of what lies beneath at the deepest lake in England, plunging 74 m (243 ft). This glacial lake in the Wasdale Valley in the Lake District – the landscape that inspired English poets William Wordsworth and Samuel Taylor Coleridge – offers a dramatic backdrop for an invigorating, if chilly, dip.

LAKE SAIMAA, FINLAND

You can swim nearly everywhere in this freshwater lake – all 4,400 square kilometres (1,699 square miles) of it. Head to a marked beach or rent a cabin in the forest. Feeling a bit Wim Hof? Visit during November to February for a spot of *avanto* – swimming in an ice hole. Finns often combine it with a blast of heat at a sauna.

CRATER LAKE, OREGON, UNITED STATES

This lake – the deepest in the United States at 582 m (1,943 ft) – was formed 7,700 years ago when Mount Mazama, a volcano, erupted and collapsed. Some Indigenous Americans suggest a battle between the gods of the sky and underworld was involved. Its colour – a rich cerulean blue – comes from the purity of the water: fed just by rain and snow, the lake lacks sediment and mineral deposits. Swimmers are welcome from mid-June to mid-September.

LAKE WAKATIPU, QUEENSTOWN, NEW ZEALAND

According to Māori legend, this lake was formed by the imprint of a *taniwha*, or giant, killed by the lover of a girl that it had kidnapped. The rise and fall of the lake is believed to be the *taniwha*'s heartbeat. The more mundane origin story is that the lake was carved out by a glacier 15,000 years ago. Its tide, or seiche, which causes the water to rise and fall, is due to the mountains around it, the wind and atmospheric pressure. Expect invigorating temperatures of 8–10°C (46–50°F), even in warmer months.

RIVER

A carefree splash in a river can be a brilliant way into wild swimming. On a warm day, you can dry off on the banks, lying back and daydreaming. Every river is different. In some places, you will encounter the gentle type, while in others, you'll meet the go-getting sort with a waterfall and plunge pool. You'll need to give the river a quick personality test before you swim in it, understanding how it reacts to rain and obstacles along its course. Is it a river for a quick dip or is it your call to adventure?

River snorkelling

Discover the secrets of a river with a
spot of snorkelling. On calm, shallow
stretches, you might stop to commune with
fish, staying still so you don't churn up
debris on the riverbed and experiencing
a sense of tranquillity. When the flow is
more active, tune into the sound of water
rushing by, as you become immersed in your
surroundings. Go with a guide for expert
knowledge or research the area first,
so you know which creatures to look out
for. Clear river water tends to be cold so,
as well as a snug-fitting snorkel mask,
consider wearing a wetsuit.

LIFE IS BETTER IN THE WATER

FIND YOUR FLOW

Navigating the flow of a river is part of the fun, but you don't want to leave it all to chance.

Remember the saying "still waters run deep"? This is because water flows faster in shallower and narrower sections of a river.

You should also consider the current as the river flows from a high point to a low point. In a straight stretch, water flows fastest in the middle, while in a meandering river, water flows fastest along the outside bend. Land features are also important. The river might mellow out as it expands into a pool or get into a frenzy as it plunges over rocks.

Rivers that flow into the sea experience tides. They tend to be more noticeable, as you might expect, near the river mouth, but they can affect the flow surprisingly far inland. For guidance, consult the local tide timetable.

To get a sense of the river, walk the length of your swim before you get in, checking the flow by throwing a leaf into the water and watching it float. Even if you plan to swim downstream with the current, make sure you can swim against it, in case you need to avoid branches, rocks or other swimmers.

Changing depths

Rivers change depth along their length and sometimes their breadth. They are shallower on the inside of a bend, where the current moves more slowly, and deeper on the outside, where it moves faster. If the river is affected by the tide, the depth can sometimes vary by several metres, so remember to check tide timetables. Plunge pools can also vary in depth, making popular jumping spots dangerous when water levels drop. Only jump in if you know it is deep enough at the time that you're there.

Three rules of waterfall plunge pools

A waterfall is a river at its most alive and there's nothing more magical than swimming in the presence of one of nature's most beautiful water displays. However, we still need to respect the unique environment.

1. Steer clear of the base of the waterfall, where the water splashes into the pool. The force of the flow, together with churning currents, can trap you underwater.

2. The higher the drop, the stronger the flow. Even if the flow of the waterfall is relatively gentle, terrain near the base could be rocky and dangerous.

3. At high flow, after heavy rain, calm pools can turn into torrents. Assess the location in the moment, even if you've swum there before.

Safe swims

Happy swims are safe swims, so keep your own safety in mind while taking the plunge in a river. Follow these tips and be sensible, and you won't go wrong:

- Check that the bank at your entry and exit points is solid and not silty.
- If you get entangled in weeds, swim out the way you swam in.
- Watch out for boats. Staying near the bank will allow you to easily get out.
- However, avoid the bank if you spot an angler, so you won't get tangled in the fishing line.
- Increase your visibility by asking a friend to kayak or paddleboard beside you.
- Avoid weirs, dams and locks, which all affect the flow of a river.

LOOK OUT
FOR SIEVES

Try taking a pre-swim walk and look out for fallen trees and branches dangling into the river that are likely to affect the flow. Obstacles like this – often called sieves or strainers – allow water through, but not swimmers. You'll want to avoid them so the water, now travelling with added force, doesn't push you against them, making it hard for you to escape. Make sure you look out for sudden ripples or waves along your chosen stretch too, as these suggest something is submerged in the water – perhaps a branch or a rock. Make a note of where they are and be sure to swim around them.

Have an exit strategy

Before getting in, plan how you'll get out. Towards the end of your swim, you might feel euphoric but tired. Consider a shelving ledge, where there are steps, and avoid high banks, rocks, moss and nettles. If your entry and exit points are the same, swim upstream first so that you push against the current at your most energetic. If you plan to get out elsewhere, locate an exit downstream. Swimming in a tidal river? Take account of changing depths by checking the tide timetable. A gentle eddy, where the water flows against the main current, can be useful. Have a back-up, just in case.

Take a hike

"Cross-country swimming" is a great way to blend key elements of nature – the land and the water. Set off on a hike, well prepared to hit the water when the opportunity arises. The idea is that when, on your trek, you reach a river that blocks your path, instead of changing route or using a bridge, you swim across it, putting your clothes in a waterproof inflatable bag or large tow float. Research your route well, planning entry and exit points in the water and checking you have permission to cross the land. Walk-swim trails are a great way to discover the environment in a new way.

ALL-WEATHER SWIMS

Many wild swimmers delight in taking to the water in all weathers. It can feel adventurous to go out when others are indoors, but rain and wind can affect you and even seasoned swimmers need to be weather-aware.

Wind

Choppy water can make swimming harder, so you'll need to take shorter, faster strokes and keep your body streamlined. To do this, focus on being long in the water, reaching for the direction you're going in with your arms. You could even imagine you're swimming through a narrow tube. Wind can also affect the flow of the water and make you feel colder more quickly.

Rain

Rain changes the flow and depth of rivers – and you could be affected even if it only rains further upstream. There might also be a delay, depending on the soil and the size of the catchment area. Stretches of water where conditions change quickly are known as flashy rivers. Avoid rivers that have burst their banks – floodwater can be forceful and move fast, carrying logs, branches and debris. Also, remember that rain can make banks slippery when you're getting in and out.

Thunderstorms

Resist the temptation to swim in a storm. Lightning strikes the tallest object it can find and, in the water, that could be you. Water also conducts electricity, so you could be electrocuted by a strike close by. If you're already in the water, swim to shore and only accept a lift from a boat if it gets you to shelter faster. Getting indoors should be your aim. It's safer to watch the storm from inside.

Fog

Fog can add a layer of Gothic drama to your swim. Some like the eeriness and say reduced visibility heightens their other senses. Keep a landmark in view to avoid getting disorientated and make sure you can see your exit point or know how long it will take to get there. A tow float with a torch and whistle to attract attention are essential.

Rivers are the great teachers... in them are all the histories and all the worlds.

MARY OLIVER

GRANTCHESTER MEADOWS, CAM, ENGLAND

Writers Virginia Woolf and Rupert Brooke went skinny-dipping here. Now you can follow in their wake – clothed. The 4-km stretch (2.5 mi) between Bryon's Pool and King's Mill Weir in Cambridge is free from motorboats, although you should still expect the odd punt.

PONT DU GARD, GARDON, NEAR NÎMES, FRANCE

This popular swimming spot features a three-tiered Roman aqueduct, 275 m long (902 ft) and nearly 50 m high (164 ft). Survey the scene from the pebble beach, before wading into the cool, shallow water.

CRYSTAL RIVER, FLORIDA, UNITED STATES

Bob along with manatees as you both enjoy the glistening water fed by hot springs and flowing into the Gulf of Mexico. The population of this friendly sea creature is at its peak between December and February, although you'll find them all year round.

ERAWAN WATERFALL, THAILAND

This seven-tiered waterfall, named after the three-headed elephant of Hindu mythology, runs from the Huai Mong Lai River. Start with a hike through the forests of Erawan National Park, looking out for great hornbills, macaques and wild boars. Aim for November to January, when the weather is drier and cooler.

SEA

The seaside is often our first love. As children, it can represent ice cream, sandcastles and splashing in the water. Even as we get older, it can offer us the opportunity to switch off and let go – when we lie on our backs and float or when we play in the waves. Our days at the beach might now mean something different from those early encounters, but they can still be just as memorable.

Water has a voice...
It tells us of its journey,
of its joys and sorrows, of
its longings and desires.

NAN SHEPHERD

Secret spots

With so many people heading to the coast on a sunny day, finding a secluded spot can sometimes feel unlikely. You could be lucky – or you could ask local people. A map or an exploration of the area can offer an initial idea for a swimming location, but you'll want trusted details before you plunge in. See what you can find out about tides and rip currents, entry points and submerged rocks, jet-skiers and boats, stingrays and weever fish. Locate your nearest contact point in case you need help and tell someone where you're about to go.

TIDAL TALK

The sea has a busy schedule, submitting to the moon's gravitational pull on the Earth, but what do the tides mean and how can they affect your swim? Here's everything you need to know:

- Every day, there are two high and two low tides, 50 minutes later than the day before.
- When a tide is coming in (flooding), it can cut you off from the shore. When it's going out (ebbing), it can be harder to swim back.
- Tidal ranges, the distance between high and low tide, can be very different. The Mediterranean and Caribbean Seas

have small tides. But at the Bay of Fundy in Canada, tides typically reach 14.5 m (47.6 ft).

- Swimming tends to be easier on a slack tide – often an hour either side of high or low water – when the water should be calmer.
- Once a fortnight, at full moon and new moon, there's a spring tide, when high tides are at their highest and low tides at their lowest. On the first and third quarter moon, a neap tide means there's less variation between high and low water.

Rip currents

Rip currents (also known as rips) are bodies of water speeding out to sea, and they can be very dangerous. They can move you away from the shore when you're not expecting it. They can also change position, so while a rip current may start at a certain point along the coast, a few hours later it could have moved to a different area.

Five ways to spot a rip current
Look for one of these signs before going in the water:
1. Fewer breaking waves
2. Ripples surrounded by smooth water
3. Deeper-coloured water

4. Debris floating out to sea
5. Sand swirling up from the seabed

Your escape plan

- Stay calm.
- Swim away from the rip. If the rip is travelling straight out to sea, move parallel to the shore. Most rips are under 25 m (27 yd) wide.
- Float by leaning back in the water. For added buoyancy, spread your arms and legs wide, look to the sky and keep your feet close to the surface. Rip currents weaken further away from shore. Floating might carry you further out, but the current will eventually cease. You will then be able to swim back.
- Tread water and signal for help.

Know your waves

A wave's power depends on the strength of the wind, the wave's fetch (how far it has travelled) and the surface of the seabed near the shore. Once you're used to swimming in open water, gentle waves can be fun to play in and you can enjoy the sea "breathing" around you. More forceful ones, however, can make moving through the water a challenge – and can be dangerous even for the strongest swimmer.

Spilling waves

Watch the crest of a spilling wave tumble playfully down its face (or front). Find them on gently sloping or flat beaches.

Plunging waves

The crest of a plunging wave moves forward faster than its base, causing it to curl over and crash down. These waves can break suddenly, so if one knocks you over, wait until its gone, before sidestepping your way towards the shore. Waves come in sets of six or seven. Before you get in, count a set. Enter and exit during the gap.

Surging waves

These are drama queens of the wave family and should be avoided where possible. They can have strong backwashes and undertows, which can sweep you out to sea. You'll find them on steep beaches or around rocky areas. (If you're wave-spotting, these are the waves that might not break as they approach the shore.)

Coral reefs

Coral reefs – colonies of tiny animals (polyps) and their limestone skeletons (calicles) – are incredible. They take up 0.1 per cent of the seabed but are home to a quarter of marine life. Yet they're at risk. We could lose 90 per cent of coral by 2050, according to conservation charity WWF, unless we slow climate change. If you visit a reef, look but don't touch. Wear reef-safe sunscreen, as chemicals such as oxybenzone, octinoxate and avobenzone can cause bleaching. This leads to coral becoming stressed and getting rid of algae living inside it, which is needed for food – and recovery from any harm can take years.

GO WHERE YOU
FEEL MOST
ALIVE

ACHMELVICH BAY, SCOTLAND

Don't be fooled by the white sand and turquoise water: this is not the Caribbean, it's north-west Scotland. In August, the hottest month, the water temperature of this part of North Atlantic averages 13°C (55°F). In March, the most shivery, it drops to 7°C (45°F). Fortunately, some like it bracing – and you do get the bonus of glimpsing a folly along the coast. The Hermit's Castle – Europe's smallest at less than 10 square metres (108 square feet) – was built by an English architect in the 1950s and then mysteriously deserted.

LOFOTEN ISLANDS, NORWAY

Join orcas and the odd moose on a swim in this archipelago in the Norwegian Sea, just above the Arctic Circle. Prepare for round-the-clock daylight from the end of May to mid-July, when the sun stays up all night. Or aim for late August to mid-April for a chance to see the Northern Lights dancing in the darkest of skies as a bonus.

ISLA DE LA PLATA, ECUADOR

While Charles Darwin plumped for the Galápagos Islands as the focus of his work, wildlife enthusiasts today head to the Isla de la Plata. The marine life is just as abundant near this island in the Pacific; the crowds, thankfully, less so. Spend time complimenting the blue-footed booby on its footwear and the male frigate bird on its inflatable red throat pouch. If you'd like to spot whales, the best time to visit is between June and September.

BOULDERS BEACH, SOUTH AFRICA

Ancient granite boulders shelter this cove from strong wind and waves, offering a calm and dreamy dip in the Indian Ocean, accompanied by the braying of 3,000 African penguins. The endangered birds live here throughout the year – a convenient 40 km (25 mi) from Cape Town for all concerned – but they are especially active on the shore from December to February. For the closest encounters, follow the walkway to Foxy Beach, a short stroll north.

NINGALOO REEF, WESTERN AUSTRALIA

The Great Barrier Reef might steal popular attention, but the Ningaloo Reef, in Western Australia, has its own appeal. At 300 km (186 mi), this is the world's largest fringing reef, much of it an easy swim from the shore. The reef in the Indian Ocean comprises 200 types of coral – from lavender corals to branching corals – and offers a colourful home and garden to 500 species of fish, manta rays, turtles and, from March to July, the whale shark, the largest omnivore in the world.

Conclusion

Now you've read this book, you may well be keen to go for a dip inspired by some of the ideas and suggestions on each page. Perhaps you're keen to head to the coast for a wave-filled sea swim, or long to plan a cross-country river adventure. Maybe you're hoping to soothe your joints or your thoughts through cold-water therapy, or are looking for a challenge and a thrill. Whatever your "why", one thing is guaranteed: wild swimming, at any time of year and whatever the temperature of the water, has much to recommend it.

While wild swimming takes more planning than a dip in your local pool – you'll need to consider entry and exit points, and currents and tides, and ensure you avoid dams, weirs and a few marine creatures – the pay-off is more than worth it. You'll get to spend time in nature, bond with friends and feel the tingle of cold water. So whether you long to feel more alive, more creative, or are curious to see whether cold water can ease stress or chronic pain, you are now well equipped to take your first step into the watery world of wild swimming. Congratulations! Your aquatic adventure awaits.

My dip list

Jot down your dream destinations, from a local river to a remote island. Then record your visits.

Local spots

Day trips

Holiday plans

Dream destinations

Destination

Date

Weather

Temperature

Swim buddy

How did it feel? Before, during, after

Comments

NATURE THERAPY

ISBN: 978-1-83799-148-8

Discover the healing power of nature with this beautiful book. Whether you find your sense of connection in the adventure of windswept cliffs, the solace of a forest, the comfort of your own garden or in the joy of tending a plant in your home, nature has the power to refresh your well-being and help you find your sense of self.

FEEL-GOOD GARDENING

ISBN: 978-1-80007-991-5

Featuring simple tips, practical advice and inspiring ideas, this book will help you discover how to reap the mental, physical and spiritual benefits found in nature.

Whether you're hoping to cultivate a calmer mindset, nurture your physical strength or connect with your community, the restorative powers of gardening can help you flourish.

Have you enjoyed this book?
If so, find us on Facebook at
Summersdale Publishers, on Twitter/X at
@Summersdale and on Instagram and TikTok
at **@summersdalebooks** and get in touch.
We'd love to hear from you!

www.summersdale.com

Image Credits

Cover image © Tero Vesalainen/Shutterstock.com; p.3, p.17, p.38, p.51, p.62, p.71, p.82, p.116, p.142 © Annykos/Shutterstock.com; pp.4–5, pp.6–7, pp.154–155, p.160 © ganjalex/Shutterstock.com; pp.8–9, pp.32–33, pp.56–57, pp.80–81, pp.106–107, pp.130–131 © donfiore/Shutterstock.com; p.10, p.35, p.43, p.60, p.67, p.78, p.89, p.114 © marukopum/Shutterstock.com; p.11, p.34, p.50, p.61, p.70, p.79, p.91, p.115 © marukopum/Shutterstock.com; pp.12–13, pp.26–27, pp.44–45, pp.68–69, pp.94–95, pp.138–139 © Naoki Kim/Shutterstock.com; pp.14–15, pp.28–29, pp.46–47, pp.76–77, pp.110–111, pp.140–141 © Angelina Bambina/Shutterstock.com; p.16 © Mourad Saadi on Unsplash; pp.18, 39, 42, 55, 63, 73, 74, 83, 108, 117, 121, 132 – photographs by Julie Goldsmith; pp.20–21, pp.36–37, pp.48–49, pp.86–87, pp.118–119, pp.134–135 © Northern Owl/Shutterstock.com; p.25, p.54, p.64, p.84, p.109, p.143 © Drekhann/Shutterstock.com; p.89 © Wren Meinberg on Unsplash; p.97 © DZiegler/Shutterstock.com; p.98 © Daniel_Kay/Shutterstock.com; p.100 © Aastels/Shutterstock.com; p.102 © Wollertz/Shutterstock.com; p.104 © S Watson/Shutterstock.com; p.122 © Mike Higginson/Shutterstock.com; p.124 © Fresnel/Shutterstock.com; p.126 © Alisia Luther/shutterstock.com; p.129 © worradirek/Shutterstock.com; p.144 © Bourne for nature/Shutterstock.com; p.146 © aroundworld/Shutterstock.com; p.148 © Ksenia Ragozina/Shutterstock.com; p.150 © KODAKovic/Shutterstock.com; p.152 © Pierre06/Shutterstock.com.